MW00892854

LUNA'S BIG OXCIDENT

By P.T. Custard
Illustrated by Amanda Rose Warren

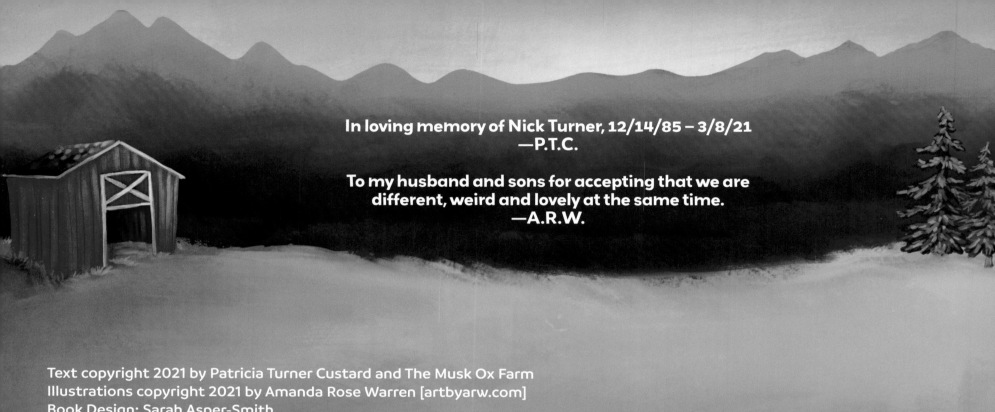

In loving memory of Nick Turner, 12/14/85 – 3/8/21
—P.T.C.

To my husband and sons for accepting that we are
different, weird and lovely at the same time.
—A.R.W.

Text copyright 2021 by Patricia Turner Custard and The Musk Ox Farm
Illustrations copyright 2021 by Amanda Rose Warren [artbyarw.com]
Book Design: Sarah Asper-Smith

All rights reserved. No part of this publication may be reproduced,
stored in retrieval or transmitted in any form or by any means
electronic, mechanical, photocopying, recording, digitizing or otherwise,
without the prior permission of The Musk Ox Farm.

Library of Congress Control Number: 2021902236

ISBN: 978-0-9785317-5-1

Published by Black Plume Books [blackplumebooks.com]
for The Musk Ox Farm
Palmer, Alaska
muskoxfarm.org

Printed in Canada by Friesens

Luna, a musk ox,
loved being part of a herd because
everyone was just like her.

And being like her was
the best thing to be!

Luna and her herd were alike in just about every way.

They looked the same. They lived in the same place.

They ate the same things.

They were born at the same time of the year.

They even all got weighed on the same day.

All this sameness was comforting to Luna, it made her feel safe. It made her feel surrounded by friends.

Seasons changed and the weather varied.

Still, life for Luna and her herd
remained unchanged.

Luna now just had three legs.

On top of that, she was stuck in some strange contraption that was meant to help her heal.

This was too much.

This was all just TOO different.

As Luna stood in her sling, she worried about being a part of the herd again.

How could she be?

Now no one else was just like her and being a part of a herd meant being the same. She was afraid she would lose the comfort of her friends.

Luna was very sad as she spent day after day alone from her herd, trying to get better.

To take her mind off her woes she began to look more closely at her herd and what she saw surprised her.

Elim is blind in one eye.

Koyuk is huge, much bigger than all the other oxen.

Maggie is small because she was born in the fall instead of the spring like all the others.

Everywhere she looked, Luna noticed differences in her herd.

She wondered why she hadn't noticed all these differences before.

As she looked closer she realized that every musk ox was different, either by a little or a lot.

As she watched more closely she saw that her herd ate together.

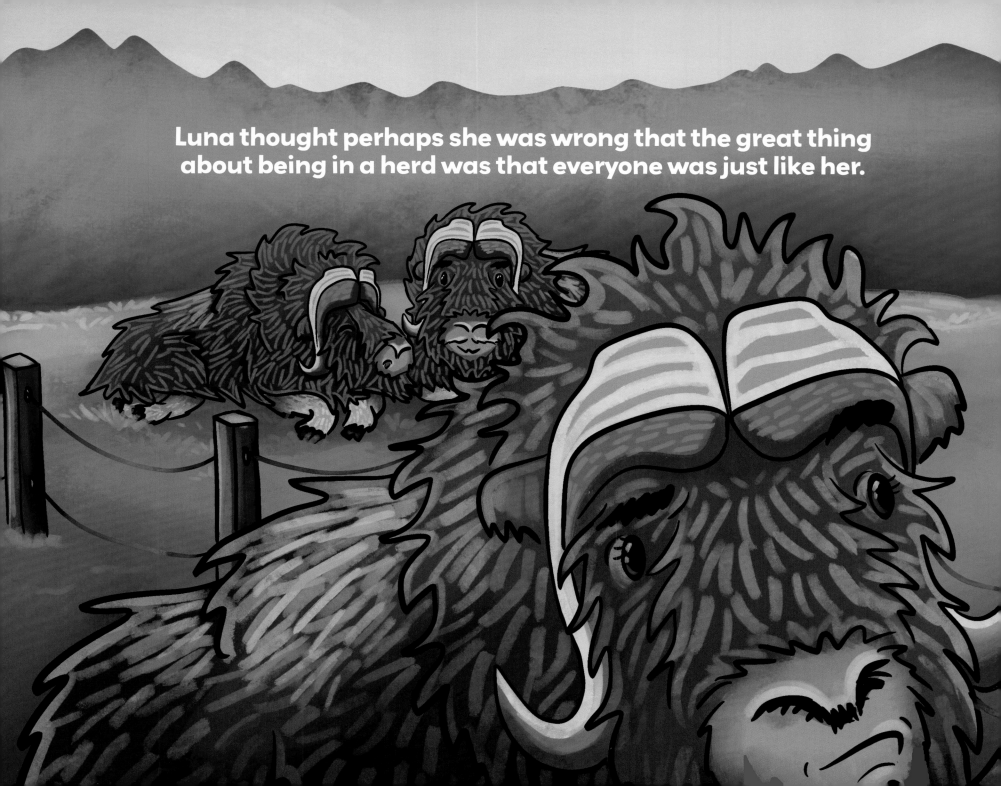

Luna thought perhaps she was wrong that the great thing about being in a herd was that everyone was just like her.

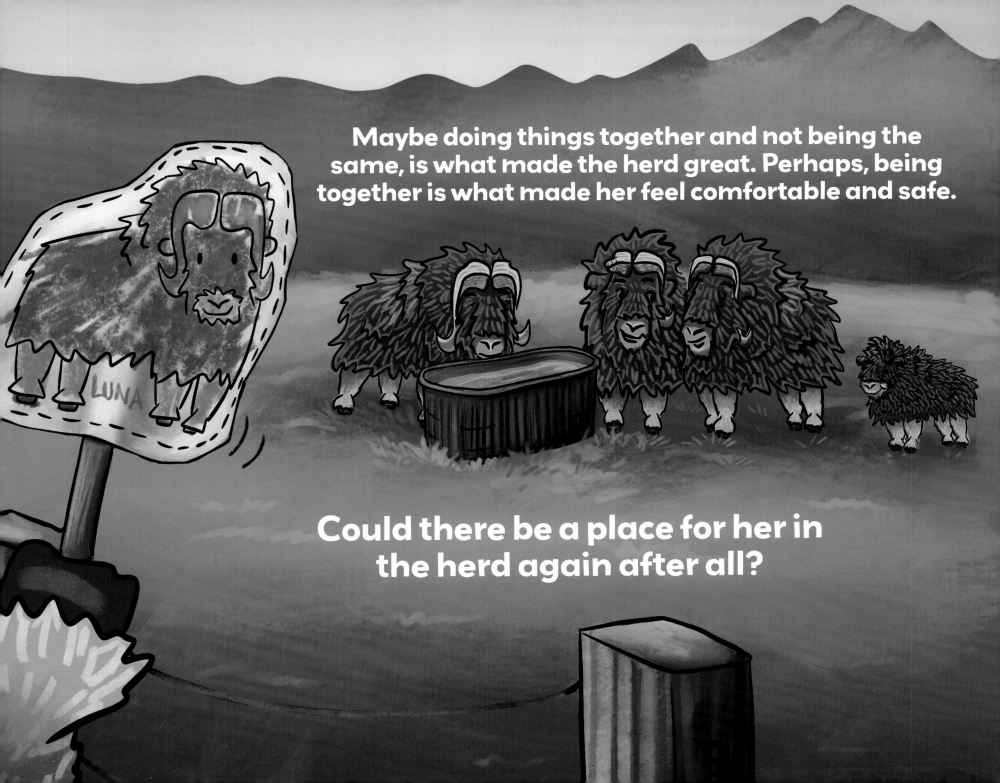

Maybe doing things together and not being the same, is what made the herd great. Perhaps, being together is what made her feel comfortable and safe.

Could there be a place for her in the herd again after all?

Finally, the day arrived when Luna could rejoin her herd.

She felt nervous and hesitant.

She was anxious and afraid.

Her mind buzzed with worry and what ifs.

What if she was just too different?

What if her friends didn't accept her?

Slowly, on three good legs, Luna approached her herd.

Slowly, all together, her herd approached her.

Soon, Luna was surrounded by all her friends. She would not be alone and scared again. Luna was happy.

Luna loves being a part of a herd because no one is just like her, but they all do things together.

Being together is the best thing to be!

ABOUT LUNA

Luna was born on April 27th, 2002. Plucky, sassy, and one of the sweetest members of the herd, Luna is also the toughest little musk ox in the whole wide world. Her gentle demeanor allowed handlers to support her rehab and physical therapy so Luna could heal and rejoin the herd.

Huge thanks to Luna's vet, Dr. Cherise Neu, and the many other veterinarians who offered their sage counsel in care. Also, the tireless and selfless care that farm staff and friends provided to Luna during the bitter winter days that slowly faded to spring and summer.

ABOUT US

In 1964, Musk Ox Farm founder, John J. Teal Jr., began a bold agricultural experiment. Teal imagined bringing geographically appropriate agriculture to the far north where it had not existed before. The project wasn't just unique in its intentional domestication of a large mammal, but in the gentle approach he championed.

Today, the nonprofit Musk Ox Development Corporation, d.b.a. The Musk Ox Farm carries on with Teal's vision of gentle and low-stress husbandry with these magnificent animals. The farm is located on 75 beautiful acres outside of Palmer, Alaska. Over 80 playful, lazy, curious musk oxen call the farm home. Raised for their incredibly soft, warm underwool (qiviut), the musk oxen on the farm are treated with kindness, respect, and dignity throughout their long lives. Visit their website: www.muskoxfarm.org where you can learn about the farm, membership, and adopt a musk ox to call your own! Or better yet, stop by and meet Luna and the rest of the herd to learn more!